FOR THE LOVE OF PEANUTS!

by Charles M. Schulz

Selected cartoons from
Good Grief, More Peanuts!
Vol. II

A Fawcett Crest Book

Fawcett Publications, Inc., Greenwich, Connecticut
Member of American Book Publishers Council, Inc.

This book, prepared especially for Fawcett Publications, Inc., comprises the second half of GOOD GRIEF, MORE PEANUTS!, and is published by arrangement with Holt, Rinehart and Winston, Inc.

Tenth Fawcett Crest printing, July 1967

Published by Fawcett World Library,
67 West 44th Street, New York, New York 10036.
Printed in the United States of America

?
SCHULZ

THAT'S THE WAY TO PITCH, CHARLIE BROWN, OL' KID!

KEEP THROWIN' 'EM, BOY! YOU'RE DOING GREAT!!
GOOD PITCHING, OL' PAL! KEEP THROWIN' 'EM IN THERE!
HEY, WAIT A MINUTE! YOU DON'T HAVE TO WALK OUT HERE EVERY TIME.. JUST THROW ME THE BALL..
LISTEN...IF THE OTHER TEAM EVER SAW ME TRYING TO THROW TO YOU....
THEY'D KNOW I COULD NEVER THROW AS FAR AS SECOND BASE!
SCHULZ

WHAT'VE YOU GOT BEHIND YOUR BACK, CHARLIE BROWN?
NONE OF YOUR BUSINESS!
I'LL BET IT'S A VALENTINE..
!
THIS IS FOR YOU VIOLET.. HAPPY VALENTINE'S DAY!
THAT DOESN'T SOUND QUITE RIGHT..
?
THIS IS FOR YOU, VIOLET.. HAPPY VALENTINE'S DAY!
HERE, VIOLET, THIS IS FOR YOU... HAPPY VALENTINE'S DAY!

I KNOW I CAN DO IT IF I JUST DON'T GET NERVOUS...
THIS IS FOR YOU, VIOLET... HAPPY VALENTINE'S DAY!
THIS IS FOR YOU VIOLET... HAPPY VALENTINE'S DAY!
OOPS! THERE SHE IS!! EASY, NOW...DON'T GET NERVOUS...YOU CAN DO IT
THIS IS FOR YOU, VIOLET... MERRY CHRISTMAS!
AAGHH!

Thump!
Thump!
Thump!
SCHULZ

ONE, TWO, THREE... THERE'S NO DOUBT ABOUT IT...I'M FIFTY YEARS AHEAD OF MY TIME..
FOUR, FIVE, SIX...
WHAT IN THE WORLD ARE YOU STANDING HERE FOR?
DON'T YOU KNOW IT'S STARTING TO RAIN?
OF COURSE, I KNOW IT! THAT'S WHY I'M HERE!! **I'M COUNTING RAINDROPS!**

'COUNTING RAINDROPS'! GOOD GRIEF! FIRST IT WAS STARS...NOW IT'S RAINDROPS!
!
OH, MY!
SCHULZ

RATS!

LUCY, WILL YOU WIND MY TRAIN FOR ME?

THANK YOU!
WHIRR

WHIRRRRRR

RRRRRRR

SCHULZ
RRRRRRRRRRR

OOPS!!
COMIX
HEH HEH
HEH
EEK!
AAK!

HEH HEH
HEH HEH

YIPE!

WHOOPS!

SOMETIMES IT'S KIND OF FUN HAVING A COLD NOSE!
SCHULZ

SCHULZ

HO HO HO HO
HEE HEE
THOSE GIRLS HAVE BEEN SITTING THERE ALL MORNING TALKING AND GIGGLING..
I'LL BET I KNOW WHAT'S GOING ON...
YOU GIRLS ARE TALKING ABOUT ME, AREN'T YOU?
?
IF YOU HAVE SOMETHING TO SAY ABOUT ME, WHY DON'T YOU SAY IT TO MY FACE?
WE WEREN'T TALKING ABOUT YOU, CHARLIE BROWN! NOW, GO AWAY!

HA HA HA HA!
HO HO HO HO HO HO!
NOW YOU'RE LAUGHING AT ME!!
OH, GOOD GRIEF! WE WEREN'T LAUGHING AT YOU! WE WEREN'T EVEN THINKING ABOUT YOU!!
HOW COME YOU GIRLS NEVER THINK ABOUT ME?
SCHULZ

COME OVER HERE BY THE CURB...
I WANT TO TELL YOU A FEW THINGS YOU SHOULD KNOW..
?
DO YOU SEE THOSE HOUSES OVER THERE, LINUS? WELL, EACH ONE HAS A FAMILY LIVING IN IT JUST LIKE OURS
AND THERE ARE THOUSANDS OF HOUSES ALL OVER THE CITY... AND THERE ARE HUNDREDS OF CITIES ALL OVER THE STATE...

AND IF YOU STARTED TO WALK, YOU'D COME TO OTHER STATES WITH MORE CITIES WITH MORE PEOPLE, AND THEN YOU'D COME TO THE OCEAN!

AND IF YOU CROSSED THE OCEAN, YOU'D COME TO MORE COUNTRIES WITH MORE PEOPLE! MILLIONS OF PEOPLE!!

AND THEN THERE ARE ANIMALS, LINUS! THE FORESTS ARE FILLED WITH ANIMALS, AND THE OCEANS ARE FILLED WITH FISH, AND THE SKY IS FILLED WITH BIRDS, AND..

AAUGHH!
SCHULZ

HOW CAN I TAKE YOUR PICTURE IF YOU'RE GOING TO SIT 'WAY OVER THERE? COME UP CLOSER..

NO, NOT THAT CLOSE! MOVE AWAY!

NOW DON'T SCOWL, SNOOPY, PLEASE!

AND DON'T GIVE ME THAT SILLY GRIN!

AND DON'T TURN YOUR HEAD! LOOK AT THE CAMERA!

TRY TO HOLD STILL, SNOOPY...FOR ONCE IN YOUR LIFE SEE IF YOU CAN COOPERATE..
JUST ACT NATURAL.. SMILE PLEASANTLY..UH,HUH. THERE! THAT'S FINE... READY?
CLICK!
OH, I CAN'T STAND IT!
?
SCHULZ

SWING, 'PIG-PEN'! SWING!
KLOP
!
GIMME THAT BALL!! HE'S GONNA SCORE! GIMME IT, I SAY!!!
RRRRRRRRRRR

BY GOLLY, I'M NOT GONNA FOOL AROUND WITH YOU!
?
HOME! HOME! GET 'IM AT HOME!
I'M SAFE!
OH, GOOD GRIEF!

YOU DRIVE ME CRAZY!
SCHULZ

TAKE IT AWAY LINUS...HAVE A GOOD TIME!
WHAT A STRANGE LITTLE FELLOW HE IS....
DID YOU KNOW THAT YOUR BROTHER BORROWED MY CROQUET SET?
WHAT'S THE MATTER, CHARLIE BROWN? YOU WANT IT BACK ALREADY?

OH, NO..
I WAS JUST WONDERING IF HE HAD ANY TROUBLE GETTING IT SET UP...
I DON'T THINK HE KNOWS ANYTHING AT ALL ABOUT CROQUET....

SCHULZ
!
BUT HE'S SURE GOOD ON THE HIGH HURDLES!

?

SCHULZ

GEE, HE'S CUTE *SIGH* BUT HE DOESN'T EVEN KNOW I'M ALIVE..
AND SOMETHING'S GOT TO BE DONE ABOUT IT!
I'M GOING TO MAKE SCHROEDER NOTICE ME IF I HAVE TO KILL MYSELF TRYING...
HEY! HEY!
?

LOOKIT ME! I'M DANCIN'!
GET OFF MY PIANO!
GOOD GRIEF! SCRATCHES..SCUFF MARKS..FOOTPRINTS..
WHEW
I THINK THAT POOR GIRL HAS LOST HER MIND..
I'LL PROBABLY NEVER GET MARRIED..
SCHULZ

RATS..
SNAP!
RATS!
SNAP!

RATS!!
SNAP!

SIGH...

I JUST LEARNED SOMETHING...
OH?

NO MATTER HOW HARD YOU TRY, YOU CAN'T BEND A CRACKER!

THUMP
THUMP
THUMP
THUMP

RIP!
CRASH!
SNAP!
TEAR!
BONK!
SMASH!

?
SCHULZ

AAUGH

SCHULZ

WHAPETY WHAPETY WHAPETY
WHAPETY WHAP

!
GLUP!

HEY! LET GO OF THAT BALL

NO! I MEAN DON'T LET GO!

ZOOM!

YOU DRIVE ME CRAZY!
SCHULZ

!
CLUMP!

HEY!

YOU CRAZY DOG!!

GOTCHA!
WHAM!

LET GO! LET GO, I SAY!! LET GO!

WHEW WHAT A STRUGGLE..

I DON'T KNOW WHAT'S WRONG WITH THESE LIBRARY RECORDS... THEY ALWAYS SOUND SCRATCHY..
SCHULZ

DUM TE DATE
DA TE DUM...
OH, OH!
I KNEW IT! EVERYTIME I BUILD A NICE SANDCASTLE PATTY COMES ALONG, AND KICKS IT TO PIECES...
WELL? WHY DOESN'T SHE GET IT OVER WITH?!!
?

THE SUSPENSE IS KILLING ME!
?
WELL, I'LL BE! SHE DIDN'T EVEN TOUCH IT! SHE DIDN'T..
!
POW!

SIGH
SCHULZ

YOU CAN'T BELIEVE EVERYTHING YOU HEAR, YOU KNOW..
WELL, YOU CAN BELIEVE THIS!
YOU KNOW I'M RIGHT, SCHROEDER..
IF YOU HAD ANY SENSE AT ALL, YOU'D ADMIT IT..
OH, YEAH? YOU JUST SAY THAT BECAUSE YOU'RE STUPID, CHARLIE BROWN!
STUPID? LISTEN TO WHO'S TALKING! YOU AND THAT PIANO OF YOURS ARE THE STUPID ONES!
PLINK PLINK PLINK!! ALL DAY LONG... GOOD GRIEF!

WELL, HOW ABOUT YOU AND THAT SILLY OL' COONSKIN CAP?!
AND HOW ABOUT THAT STUPID SHIRT WITH THAT STUPID STRIPE?!
WELL, AT LEAST, SCHROEDER, I DON'T HAVE YELLOW HAIR!
NO, BUT YOU SURE HAVE A ROUND HEAD!
WHAT IN THE WORLD IS GOING ON HERE?
WE'RE ARGUING OVER WHO WAS THE BETTER...BEETHOVEN OR DAVY CROCKETT!
WHO'S GOT A ROUND HEAD?
YOU HAVE!
?
SCHULZ

KLUNK!

SCHULZ

YOU STAND THERE, AND I'LL STAND RIGHT OVER HERE...
?
NOW YOU DO JUST WHAT I TELL YOU..
JUMP SNOOPY! JUMP!
NO! NO! NO! THROUGH THE HOOP! THROUGH THE HOOP!

COME ON NOW... JUMP THROUGH THE HOOP..YOU CAN DO IT...
AH! I THINK HE'S GOT THE IDEA...HE'S GOING BACK TO GET A GOOD RUNNING START..
C'MON, SNOOPY! THAT'S THE BOY!! JUMP!!
SCHULZ

GIMME THAT MAGAZINE! THAT'S MY MAGAZINE!

!

BANG BANG BANG!

Mommy!
BANG BANG BANG BANG
BANG! BANG!

LINUS KEEPS SHOOTING ME! MAKE HIM QUIT IT!!
BANG! BANG! BANG!
BANG BANG
LINUS! YOU STOP THAT NOW!! BEHAVE YOURSELF!
AND PUT THAT GUN AWAY!

SIGH
SCHULZ

AN' TWO FINGERS WILL MEAN A 'DROP,' AN' THREE FINGERS WILL MEAN AN 'UPSHOOT,' AN'...
WE'LL NEVER REMEMBER ALL THOSE SIGNALS, BUT IT WON'T MAKE ANY DIFFERENCE BECAUSE HE CAN'T THROW ANY OF THOSE PITCHES..
!
WHOP!
!
POW

THAT MAKES THE SCORE NINETY-THREE TO NOTHING...
I'VE COME OUT TO HAVE ANOTHER CONFERENCE WITH YOU
WHAT DO YOU THINK WE OUGHT TO DO?
WELL, THE WAY I SEE IT, THERE'S NOT TOO MUCH TO WORRY ABOUT...
I'VE GOT A FEELING THAT THEY WON'T BE HITTING 'EM SO FAR ANY MORE...
WE'RE CATCHING ON TO THEIR WEAKNESSES, HUH?
NO, THE COVER IS ABOUT TO COME OFF THE BALL!
SCHULZ

YOU AND YOUR STUPID OL' BEETHOVEN!

SCHROEDER NEVER PAYS ANY ATTENTION TO ME...WELL, BY GOLLY, I'LL SHOW HIM! YES, SIR!

CHARGE!

SMASH

THERE!
WHAT DO YOU THINK OF THAT?
?
!

I'LL PROBABLY NEVER GET MARRIED...
SCHULZ

WHAM!

WELL? WHAT DO YOU THINK? SHALL WE DO SOMETHING ELSE FOR AWHILE?
WE MIGHT AS WELL...LET'S GO OVER TO MY HOUSE FOR SOME LEMONADE..
WHEW!
WHEN? WHEN? WHEN? WHEN? WHEN? WHEN? WHEN?

WHEN WILL I EVER LEARN?!
SCHULZ

HMM...

YOU KNOW WHAT? CHOMP-CHOMP-CHOMP.
WHAT?

NO MATTER HOW HARD YOU TRY YOU CAN'T THROW A POTATO CHIP!
SCHULZ

WHAM

SCHULZ
YOU'RE THE ONLY PERSON I KNOW WHO CAN USE UP A WHOLE DAY IN FIVE MINUTES!

GET 'WAY OUT, LINUS...
'WAY OUT!

GOOD GRIEF!
SCHULZ

IT'S FUNNY...EVERYTIME THE THERMOMETER GOES WAY UP, IT GETS REAL HOT OUTSIDE
WHEN IT'S AS HOT AS IT IS TODAY, THERE'S NOTHING BETTER THAN SITTING IN A POOL OF COOL WATER
I'LL GO PUT MY SWIMMING TRUNKS ON NOW, AND THEN I'LL RELAX
HEY! GET OUT OF THERE!!
OF ALL THE CRAZY DOGS!!
!
NOW I HAVE TO EMPTY THIS, AND START ALL OVER!

THERE! IT'S FULL AGAIN...BUT WHAT A JOB THAT WAS!
NOW, I'LL GO TURN OFF THE WATER,..
AND GET RIGHT BACK BEFORE...
SCHULZ

HERE IT IS, THE FIRST DAY OF WINTER, AND THERE'S NOT A BIT OF SNOW ON THE GROUND!
I CAN'T THINK OF ANYTHING MORE DISGUSTING
?
A SNOWFLAKE! IT'S STARTING TO SNOW!!

HEY, EVERYBODY! IT'S SNOWING!!

GET YOUR SLEDS! GET YOUR SKIS! GET YOUR TOBOGGANS! WINTER IS HERE! IT'S SNOWING!!

WINTER IS HERE!
WINTER IS HERE!!

SCHULZ

HEY CHARLIE BROWN! I THOUGHT WE WERE GONNA MAKE A SNOWMAN?!
I CHANGED MY MIND.. IT'S TOO COLD...
NO MATTER HOW MUCH I WEAR, I STILL GET COLD.. I MUST HAVE THIN BLOOD...
WHUMP!
?

GOOD GRIEF! I'VE GOT SO MANY CLOTHES ON, I CAN'T MOVE! I CAN'T GET UP!
WHEW IT'S NO USE... I'M DOOMED... I'LL NEVER GET HOME.. I'LL HAVE TO LIE HERE UNTIL I FREEZE TO DEATH....
THIS IS THE MOST EMBARRASSING THING THAT'S EVER HAPPENED TO ME!
SCHULZ

BANG! I GOT YOU!!
YOU DID NOT! YOU DID NOT!
BANG! BANG! BANG!!
YOU MISSED! YOU MISSED! YOU MISSED!
BANG! I GOT YOU!
YOU DID NOT!
BANG! BANG! BANG!!
I GOT YOU!
BANG! BANG! YOU DID NOT!!

BANG! I GOT YOU! WHY DON'T YOU FALL DOWN?!
WHY SHOULD I ?!! I GOT YOU FIRST!
YOU DID NOT!
I DID, TOO!
YOU CERTAINLY HAVE FUN PLAYING COWBOY AND INDIAN, DON'T YOU, CHARLIE BROWN?
I CAN'T STAND THE GAME...
IT'S THE ARGUING THAT I LIKE!
SCHULZ

HEY! HOW ABOUT GETTING IN THE GAME?
GO AWAY!
I'VE GOT MY OWN MARBLE..
WELL, 'HURRAY' FOR YOU!
IF LUCY WANTS TO PLAY, LET'S LET HER PLAY...SHE CAN'T HURT ANYTHING..
THANK YOU, CHARLIE BROWN.. WHAT DO I DO?
JUST TRY TO KNOCK THE MARBLES OUT OF THE RING.

RATS..

RATS!

RATS!

WHAT A STUPID GAME!
STOMP!STOMP!STOMP!STOMP!
STOMP! STOMP!

"LET'S LET HER PLAY... SHE CAN'T HURT ANYTHING"
SCHULZ

CRUNCH
?

RIP!

!
SCHULZ

I OUGHT TO KNOW...I SAW IT ON TELEVISION!

SEE? IT SAYS SO RIGHT HERE IN THIS BOOK! SEE?

WHAT DO YOU THINK OF THAT, SMARTY? HUH? SMARTY, SMARTY, SMARTY !!

TWANG!
SCHULZ

HOW CAN I PRACTICE WITH YOU LEANING ON THE PIANO ALL THE TIME?!
GOOD GRIEF! YOU SURE ARE A NUISANCE!
WHY CAN'T YOU BE MORE FRIENDLY TOWARD ME, SCHROEDER?
I'M ALWAYS FRIENDLY TOWARD **YOU**...I TRY TO BE WHAT YOU WANT ME TO BE...
!

AND YET, YOU NEVER EVEN **SMILE** AT ME...

COULDN'T YOU AT LEAST GIVE ME A LITTLE SMILE?

SIGH I'LL PROBABLY NEVER GET MARRIED...
SCHULZ

C'MON...LET 'IM HIT IT!
WADDYA THINK I'M OUT HERE FOR?
!

SCHULZ

WHERE IN THE WORLD DO YOU SUPPOSE THEY'RE GOING?
THIS IS A GOOD PLACE...
O.K., LINUS...NOW WE PUT ON OUR DARK GLASSES, AND WE LOOK AT THE SUN...
?
DO YOU SEE IT? IT'S ECLIPSING! IT'S ECLIPSING! ISN'T THAT MARVELOUS?
OH GOOD GRIEF!

NOW, WHEN YOU TAKE OFF YOUR GLASSES, THE ECLIPSE STOPS... SEE ?
I CAN'T STAND IT!

NOW, PUT 'EM ON AGAIN... SEE? IT'S ECLIPSING! IT'S ECLIPSING!
POOR LINUS...

HE'LL HAVE TO GO TO SCHOOL TWICE AS LONG AS EVERYBODY ELSE...

IT'LL TAKE HIM TWELVE YEARS TO UNLEARN EVERYTHING LUCY'S BEEN TEACHING HIM!
SCHULZ

HEY!
?
SNOOPY! DROP THAT BALL!
COME BACK HERE!
!
DROP IT, I SAY!

LUCY!!
STOP HIM!

DROP IT!

LUCY STUNS 'EM WITH SOUND WAVES!
SCHULZ

WHOSE TURN IS IT?
I WANT A MALLET THAT MATCHES MY DRESS...
IF I CAN'T HAVE A RED MALLET, I'M NOT GOING TO PLAY!
KLUNK
WE DON'T CARE IF YOU PLAY OR NOT!
I REGARD MYSELF AS BEING THE BEN HOGAN OF CROQUET..
I GUESS WE ALL KID OURSELVES ONE WAY OR ANOTHER..
KLUNK!
RATS! WHAT A SHOT!
CHARLIE BROWN, I'M GOING TO KNOCK YOUR BALL CLEAR OUT OF THE YARD!
WHY DO YOU ALWAYS PICK ON ME?
WHY DO YOU ALWAYS KNOCK MY BALL AWAY?!
RATS!!!
KLUNK!

IT'S PERSONAL, ISN'T IT? YOU DON'T LIKE ME, DO YOU?
ALL I'M THINKING ABOUT IS THE GAME...
KLUNK!
RIGHT NOW, CHARLIE BROWN, YOU ARE NOTHING MORE TO ME THAN A SMALL, BLUE, WOODEN BALL!
KLUNK!
WELL, I'VE FINALLY REACHED A CONCLUSION..
NO MATTER HOW HARD YOU TRY, YOU JUST CAN'T BOUNCE A CROQUET BALL!
SCHULZ

SNOOPY
WHAT IN THE WORLD IS GOING ON OVER THERE?
?

SNOOPY

SNOOPY
?
SNOOPY
HEY! IS THERE ROOM FOR ONE MORE?
SURE.. COME ON IN!

THE HOUSE ITSELF ISN'T SO BIG, BUT YOU OUGHT TO SEE THE RECREATION ROOM!
SCHULZ

WHY SHOULD WE ALWAYS DO WHAT SHE WANTS?
THAT'S WHAT I SAY!
THEN LET'S TELL HER!
LUCY, WE'VE DECIDED WE'RE NOT GOING TO PLAY YOUR WAY!
YOU'RE NOT?
WAAH!
IT'S NOT FAIR!

WHAAH!
CHEATERS!
CHEATERS!
CHEATERS!
Thump! Thump!
BAM
BAM
WHAA!

WELL THEN LET'S PLAY YOUR WAY!
SCHULZ

THIS LOOKS LIKE A GOOD SPOT..
YOU BUILD YOUR SNOW FORT 'WAY OVER THERE LINUS, AND I'LL BUILD MINE HERE..
LET ME KNOW WHEN YOU'RE READY, AND WE'LL HAVE A BIG BATTLE..
♫

AH! AN IMPREGNABLE FORTRESS OF SNOW!
THAT POOR LITTLE KID WILL BE SICK WITH JEALOUSY WHEN HE SEES WHAT I'VE BUILT...

I'M NOT READY..
SCHULZ

?
OH, GOOD GRIEF!

WHEE
WHEN? WHEN? WHEN? WHEN? WHEN WILL I EVER LEARN?
SCHULZ

PSST, CHARLIE BROWN!
?
WHAT'S UP?
PSSTSSP PSSP..
PSSTPSSP SSPSST..
PSSPST PSSP..
PSSP PST..
WHY?

PSSPPTSS..
WHY?
PSSSPSST
WHY?
PSSPSST..
WHY?
PSSPST!
PSSPT!
PSSPSST
BECAUSE!

OH..
SCHULZ

NOTICE ANYTHING PECULIAR?
NOT A THING!
I WAS AFRAID OF THAT...
IT'S STARTING TO RAIN, CHARLIE BROWN...
WHO CARES? A LITTLE RAIN NEVER HURT ANYBODY!
Y'GOTTA ADMIRE THAT CHARLIE BROWN..HE MAY BE AN IDIOT, BUT Y'GOTTA ADMIRE HIM..

YOU'RE SURE YOU DON'T WANNA GO HOME?
OF COURSE, I'M SURE!!
JUST THOUGHT I'D ASK, THAT'S ALL.. NO HARM IN JUST ASKING
YOU KNOW WHAT, CHARLIE BROWN?
WHAT?!
I DON'T THINK THE OTHER TEAM IS GOING TO SHOW UP..
SCHULZ

LUCY IS THE NATION'S FOREMOST AUTHORITY ON JUMPING ROPES
PEOPLE ARE ALWAYS COMING TO ME FOR ADVICE..
TO SOME PEOPLE .. INSURANCE AGENTS FOR EXAMPLE ... I RECOMMEND THE OWNING OF TWO JUMPING-ROPES IN CASE THEY WISH TO ENTERTAIN A CLIENT...
COULD YOU GIVE US SOME POINTERS ON ROPE-JUMPING, LUCY?
HMM..
WELL,... A LOT DEPENDS, OF COURSE, ON THE INDIVIDUAL... SOME GOT IT, AND SOME HAVEN'T..

IT'S A GOOD IDEA TO START SLOWLY... JUMPING WITH THE WIND...
IT'S VERY DANGEROUS TO JUMP IN A CROSS-WIND
I SUPPOSE WE SHOULD BE TAKING NOTES...
KEEP YOUR EYES STRAIGHT AHEAD... USE A REGULAR MOTION UNTIL YOU PICK UP SPEED...
AND THEN... GIVE 'ER TH' GUN!
OH,... THERE'S ONE OTHER THING I SHOULD HAVE MENTIONED...

NEVER JUMP TOO LONG IN THE SAME PLACE!
SCHULZ

ALL ABOARD!
DING! DING!
WE'RE COMING TO THE CROSSING!
TOOT! TOOT!
CHOO! CHOO!
CLANG! CLANG!
?!
WHEE!!
?!
WHAM!

WHAT A DIRTY TRICK!
THE MORE I THINK ABOUT THAT, THE MADDER I GET!
WHO DOES SHE THINK SHE IS, ANYWAY?! BY GOLLY, I'M GOING TO TELL HER OFF! I'M REALLY GOING TO TELL HER OFF!!!
AH! THERE YOU ARE!
YOU-YOU-YOU GIRL, YOU!!
SCHULZ

SNOOPY
ARF! ARF!
ARF!!
SNOOPY
?
SNOOPY

!
GROWF!
KLUNK!

SNOOPY
SCHULZ

?
GO TAKE A LOOK AT CHARLIE BROWN.. I THINK HE'S LOST HIS MIND!
WHAT IN THE WORLD ARE YOU DRAGGING AROUND, CHARLIE BROWN?
THIS IS A 'SECURITY AND HAPPINESS' BLANKET..ALL LITTLE KIDS CARRY THEM..
THEY'RE JUST THE THING TO HAVE WHEN YOU'RE TIRED AND DISCOURAGED...
SEE? YOU JUST SORT OF SCRUNCH YOUR FACE INTO IT, AND RIGHT AWAY YOU FEEL SECURE..

THERE'S NOTHING LIKE IT, I TELL YOU...FEEL HOW SOFT IT IS?
UH, HUH..
LOOK..HERE COMES SCHROEDER...SEE HOW SECURE AND HAPPY HE IS?
BUT I DON'T SEE ANY BLANKET..
WHAT DO YOU CALL THIS?
HEY!

SECURITY AND HAPPINESS!!
SCHULZ

LET'S GET OUT HERE IN THE OPEN WHERE WE WON'T HURT ANYBODY...
?
I GUESS THIS IS ALL RIGHT...
OKAY, LUCY...NOW TOSS THE RECORD IN THE AIR...

BANG!
IS THERE A HOLE IN THE CENTER?
OF COURSE..

FASTEST GUN IN THE WEST!
SCHULZ

HEY, LUCY! C'MON, AN' PLAY IN THE POOL!
NOPE.. I'M READING...
THIS IS SENSATIONAL!
HEY, LUCY! COME, AND JUMP ROPE!
NOT NOW... I DON'T WANT TO DO ANYTHING BUT READ MY BOOK..

THIS IS THE BEST BOOK I'VE EVER READ!
IT'S CALLED 'THE THREE LITTLE KITTENS WHO LOST THEIR MITTENS, AND IT'S ALL ABOUT THESE THREE KITTENS, SEE?
I'VE NEVER READ A BOOK THAT I'VE ENJOYED SO MUCH...
WHAT OTHER BOOKS HAVE YOU READ?

THIS IS THE ONLY ONE!
SCHULZ

HMM..
SIGH!
HI, YOU CUTE LITTLE DOGGIE...
PAT PAT
GEE, I WISH SOMEONE WOULD HUG ME LIKE THAT!
MMMMM
WELL, MAYBE SOMEONE WOULD IF YOU'D CLEAN UP ONCE IN A WHILE....PIG-PEN!!

I SAID, 'MAYBE'..

OH, WELL...IT'S KIND OF NICE TO BE FREE AGAIN!
SCHULZ

SCHULZ

YAHOO!!
GO TO IT, SNOOPY! GO TO IT!!
FASTER! FASTER! FASTER!
C'MON, SNOOPY!
YIPPEE!
THAT'S MY BOY!
SAY.... IT'S GETTING LATE...

I'VE GOT TO BE GOING HOME
ME, TOO
I DIDN'T REALIZE IT WAS SO LATE
?
THERE THEY GO... LEAVING ME ALONE AGAIN! DO ANY OF THEM EVER INVITE ME OVER TO SPEND THE NIGHT? NO!
ALL I'M GOOD FOR IS A FEW LAUGHS!
RATS!
THEY'RE WILLING TO HAVE ME ENTERTAIN THEM DURING THE DAY, BUT AS SOON AS IT STARTS GETTING DARK, THEY ALL GO OFF, AND LEAVE ME!
WELL, I'LL SHOW 'EM!.....I DON'T NEED THEIR COMPANY!
I CAN ALWAYS SIT HOME, AND WATCH TELEVISION!
SNOOPY
SCHULZ

HE'S SO CUTE, AND I'M SO MISERABLE.. HE DOESN'T KNOW I EVEN EXIST..
SIGH
HEY!!
WHY DON'T YOU FORGET ABOUT THAT STUPID PIANO FOR AWHILE, AND PAY SOME ATTENTION TO ME?

LOOK, SCHROEDER...LOOK...CAN A STUPID OL' PIANO EVER COMPARE WITH A PRETTY FACE? HUH? CAN IT? HMMMMMMM?
C'MON...FORGET ABOUT BEETHOVEN FOR AWHILE...
HOW ABOUT COMING OVER TO MY HOUSE FOR HOT CHOCOLATE AND MARSHMALLOWS?
NO!
BONG!
I'LL PROBABLY NEVER GET MARRIED!
SCHULZ

OH OH..
WHAT'S THE MATTER?
I'M RUNNING OUT OF KITE-STRING LUCY.. WILL YOU SEE WHAT YOU CAN FIND?
DOES IT HAVE TO BE REAL KITE-STRING?
NO! ANYTHING YOU CAN FIND!! ANYTHING!
HURRY!
I GOT A FEW THINGS HERE THAT SHOULD HELP, CHARLIE BROWN..
GOOD..TIE 'EM ON..
?

!
?
?
AAUGH!
CLANK

YOU DRIVE ME CRAZY!
SCHULZ

OH, OH..
C'MON.. LET'S HAVE THE BALL..
ON WITH THE GAME!
HEY! WHERE'S EVERYBODY GOING?
YOU'RE NOT GOING TO LET A LITTLE RAIN BOTHER YOU, ARE YOU?!

COME ON BACK! IT'S GOING TO CLEAR UP!
COME ON BACK!
COWARDS! QUITTERS!
RATS!

HEY, CHARLIE BROWN!! -- AREN'T YOU COMING WITH ME?
TOMORROW MAYBE, BUT NOT TODAY..
?
SOMETIMES I JUST LIKE TO BE ALONE..
SOMEDAY I'LL PROBABLY GO AWAY...I'LL GO SO FAR AWAY NOBODY WILL EVER SEE ME AGAIN...

GEE, IT'S KIND OF LONESOME WAY OUT HERE
I WAS WRONG! I GUESS I'M JUST NOT THE KIND TO BE ALONE..
THIS IS WHERE I BELONG! THIS IS WHAT I LIKE..
THE HUSTLE AND BUSTLE OF THE CITY!
SCHULZ

NO!
OH, COME ON, CHARLIE BROWN..BE A GOOD SPORT..

BE A GOOD SPORT ?!

WHY SHOULD I PLAY CHECKERS WITH SOMEONE WHO'S BEATEN ME EIGHT THOUSAND GAMES IN A ROW?

WELL, I'M TRYING TO MAKE IT AN EVEN TEN THOUSAND

COME ON, CHARLIE BROWN.. YOU HAVEN'T GOT ANYTHING ELSE TO DO...

OH, ALL RIGHT... GO AHEAD..... START ANOTHER GAME..
GOOD.. I ENJOY PLAYING SO MUCH.. EVEN IF YOU DO GET MAD WHEN YOU LOSE..
BEAT AGAIN! HA HA HA WELL, THAT'S THE WAY IT GOES, I GUESS... EIGHT THOUSAND AND THREE GAMES IN A ROW..
SHALL I STAND BACK NOW WHILE YOU RANT AND RAVE?
WHY, NO... WHY SHOULD I RANT AND RAVE? IT'S ONLY A GAME.. HA! HA! I DON'T MIND.. HA! HA! IT'S ONLY A GAME.. HA! HA!
I QUIT!!!! I HATE PLAYING WITH A POOR LOSER...
BUT I CAN'T STAND PLAYING WITH A GOOD LOSER!
SCHULZ